LAUGH WITH THE NAVY TOO!

By
Jim Swift

Can I touch your collar for luck Jack?

He wanted to take my arm off!

Right men . . .
The MOD have decided to bring back flogging . . .
They're flogging the Ark Royal . . . Norfolk . . .
Tidepool . . . Endurance

**Golly, if you're in the Reserves,
what's the first team like!**

It makes no difference, you're still not suitable for promotion!

**I'd be a lot less concerned about your obvious lack
of physical fitness if you wasn't the ship's P.T.I!**

I can tell the weather with this bit of seaweed . . .
when its wet its raining — when it swings its windy!

I wish they'd give us more notice before deciding to change the ship's operational programme!

**That's 200 duty frees for my daughter's hand . . .
what will you give me for an arm or a leg!**

**After intensive training you'll be able to kill people
with your bare hands . . . but you have to wait until
we tell you!**

**Commander in Chief nothing, that's the
Canteen Manager's car**

**Yeah, I know even Nelson got seasick . . .
but in dry dock?**

**You will be going on a long journey . . .
perhaps over water!**

I'd have no objection to naming your child after all the famous naval heroes — if it wasn't a girl!

**Don't try and kid me son, it's a bat,
not an Australian parrot!**

**Don't you think you're taking this fishery protection
a bit too seriously!**

**How long is it since they stopped the rum ration?
. . . in seconds or minutes?**

Hey lads, thanks for the lift!

You know him — Is he in the same Mess as you?

Colliding with an iceberg was bad enough — but we were supposed to be on a cruise of the West Indies!

I hated my parents, they were both civilians!

We'll accept you, some ship's bound to need
a mascot!

Fifty quid fine? . . . American Express?

Having you up before me as a defaulter will do the ship's company's morale the world of good . . . Master-at-arms!

**You won't hear me moaning about conditions . . .
I'm a stowaway!**

I'm picking you up for a haircut!

No madam, I don't flog my sailors . . . you can
have one for nothing!

**I joined for the adventure, uniform, sport . . .
and as an alternative to a shot-gun wedding!**

Alright, you may start a union, so long as you ask no one else to join!

Did I miss you? . . . why, have you been away?

**They don't make 'em like you anymore . . .
they can't get the wood!**

The food on here is really bad . . . 50 cases of scurvy and we haven't even left harbour yet!

OK! So it can't talk . . . can you lay eggs!

Apart from that, did you enjoy your trip dear?

**Pleased to see ya — we're survivors from a
tramp steamer!**

Captain . . . we've found a woman onboard!

Don't worry, they're man-eaters — so they won't touch you my lad!

Crisps? . . . snail or frog flavoured?

Say 'Please'!

I've heard you're great at pulling birds . . . show me
what you're like at pulling oars!

I don't remember giving you permission to grow
a pig tail!

**See, I told you my missus was a big woman . . .
they had to take the wedding photos from the air!**

Divorce me for anything you like Cynthia, — but never desertion!

Let's hope you don't run out of skin before you run out of girl friends!

**That's the great thing about cooking for the Navy . . .
the clientele is expendable!**

You have a full set of healthy teeth . . . trouble is they're all on the bottom!

**Me and yer dad had a good laugh when we read
what you wrote about an eye witness account of a
head shrinking ceremony in New Guinea dear!**

**I fought hard for these medals . . . the bloke in the
second hand shop put up a heck of a struggle before
he let them go!**

It's ridiculous . . . how can I lie about my age
with a good conduct badge on my arm!

The parrot's alright, it's you who has to go into quarantine!

If we ever run out of fuel Chief, we can always wring out your overalls!

Try the Royal Yacht son, you get some really great gash on there!

**We used 'em instead of pigeons in the war, saved
writin' the messages!**

It's the only way to get the men to watch it!

Come on lad, we'll soon knock you into shape!

**What are you after . . . compassionate leave
or an oscar?**

Can I borrow your uniform tonight, Dad?

**No, I'm not back from a long separation —
It's like this every payday!**

Me and yer dad made a lot of sacrifices to send you to that Naval College son!

**And I've brought your mum a lovely fur coat dear,
but she'll have to skin it herself!**

We'll go down here, they always put the good places out of bounds!

They'll have to bury you at sea Chief — it's the only place big enough!

I'll read what I've said about you . . . just
the clean bits!

**When I want your opinion, I'll read the
Gunnery Manual!**

I can't kiss you goodnight — it'll take a couple of
hours to find your lips!

There's been a complaint from the management. Can
I see your I.D. card . . . please . . . your Excellency!

**My father's ex Navy . . . his father's ex Navy . . .
and I want to be ex Navy too!**

**It's the Defence cuts . . . you'll have to reduce
manpower to 5 admirals per ship!**

I was always fascinated by criminals and crime . . .
here's an identikit photo of my parents!

This is the spot where the admiral fell, and over
there is where he got up again!

**Sure you get punchups at weddings . . . but with
the vicar!**

Don't laugh mate, she'll be your pin up too when you've been here as long as me!

**What would I give a sailor who'd drunk 18 pints of
stout, and eaten vast quantities of curry! . . .
plenty of room!**

Burial at sea for you is definitely out Chief . . . I'd be concerned about the pollution!

Does the M.O.D. know you're carrying out experiments on live human beings!

Door!

**Of course we time the eggs when we boil them . . .
what do you think that calendar's for!**

I'm normally addressed as the Officer in Charge, Royal Naval Air Station, Yorkshire, but now that you're married to my daughter, you may call me sir!

**OK, so you're the Captain's blue-eyed boy,
but nobody gets four good conduct badges!**

Look, I was happily married for 15 years, then the family welfare forced me to go home on leave!

Give me one good reason why I should excuse you Divisions!

**Cut down on the booze, fags and birds or you'll
never see your naval pension . . . padre!**

**We stoped using midget submarines years ago . . .
we ran out of midgets!**

**Your grandad fought with the Navy in the war . . .
but they got him to wear his uniform in the end!**

Hurry it up, we haven't got long . . . my ship sails in six months time!

**He says the malaria's terrible where he is . . . even
the mosquitos are dying of it!**

What's happened to that slim, freckle-faced boy who left here 12 short weeks ago?

The food's bad on 'ere mate . . . even the chief cook gets his wife to send him food parcels!

If we all clubbed together we could buy a guided missile destroyer and run it ourselves!

Does this train stop at Waterloo? There's going to be a dirty great smash up if it don't!

Pity my missus ain't here . . . she could have given them the kiss of life . . . all at the same time!